THE NEW BASIC READERS

CURRICULUM FOUNDATION SERIES

REG. U.S. PAT. OFF.

Guess Who

William S. Gray, A. Sterl Artley,
May Hill Arbuthnot

Illustrated by Corinne Boyd Dillon

SCOTT, FORESMAN AND COMPANY
Chicago · Atlanta · Dallas · New York

Stories

Dick

Look, Dick.

Look, look.

Oh, oh.

Look, Dick.

Oh, oh.

See Dick.

Oh, see Dick.

Sally

Look, Sally.

Look, look.

See Jane.

Oh, Jane.

See Sally.

See little Sally.

Little, little Sally.

Look, Jane.

See funny Sally.

Oh, oh, oh.

Funny little Sally.

Help, Help

Look, Dick.

See Spot.

Oh, see Spot.

Help, help.

Oh, Jane.

See Spot.

Oh, see Spot.

Come, Jane, come.

Help, help, help.

Look, Dick.

See Spot and Sally.

Come and see Sally.

See funny little Sally.

Sally Sees Something

Come, Sally.

Come and look.

Come and see Sally.

Funny little Sally.

Dick, Dick.

Help, help.

I see something.

Help, help, help.

I see something.

Look, Sally.

I see something.

I see Baby Sally.

Little Baby Sally.

Look, look.

See funny Baby Sally.

Something Funny

Look, Dick.

Look, look.

I see something funny.

Come and see.

Come and see Spot.

Oh, Jane.

I see something funny.

Come, Jane, come.

See Spot and Baby Sally.

Come and help.

Look, Dick.

See Jane help Spot.

Oh, see something funny.

See little Spot.

Funny little Spot.

Jane and Puff

Oh, Jane.

I see something.

Look, Jane, look.

Look here.

Come, Puff.

Come here.

Jump, little Puff.

Jump, jump.

Look, Baby Sally.

Come here and look.

See Puff.

Puff can help.

Puff can help Jane.

See Puff Go

Come here, Dick.

Come and see Puff.

See Puff play.

See Puff jump.

Puff can jump and play.

Oh, Mother, Mother.

Come and look.

See Puff jump and play.

See little Puff play.

Look, Mother, look.

See Puff jump and play.

Oh, oh, oh.

See Puff jump down.

See Puff jump and go.

Jump down, funny Puff.

Jump down.

Jump down.

Go, go, go.

Tim and Sally Help

Sally said, "Look, Mother.

I can help.

See Baby Sally help.

See little Tim help.

See little Tim go.

Oh, see little Tim go."

Sally said, "Look, Tim.
Look down here.
I see cookies.
I see cookies down here.
Cookies, cookies, cookies."

Sally said, "Come, Mother.

We can go.

Look here, Mother.

Cookies, cookies, cookies.

Come, Mother, come.

We can go."

Go Away, Spot

Dick said, "Down, Spot.

I can not play.

Down, Spot, down.

Go away, little Spot.

Go away and play."

Sally said, "Oh, Spot.

We see you.

Tim and I see you.

And little Puff sees you.

We see you, funny Spot."

Dick said, "Oh, oh, oh.
Go away, Spot.
You can not help.
You can not play here."

Sally said, "Run away, Spot.
Run, run, run."

Puff, Tim, and Spot

Sally said, "See Puff go.

Puff can jump down.

Puff can run away.

See little Tim.

Tim can not jump down.

Tim can not run away."

Dick said, "Come, Spot.
You and I can play.
Look here, Spot.
Cookies, cookies.
Jump, Spot, jump."

Dick said, "See Spot.
Oh, see Spot jump."

Jane said, "Mother, Mother.
We see something funny.
Come here.
Come here.
Come and see Spot."

Find Dick

Jane said, "I see you.

I see you, Sally.

I can find you.

I can not find Dick.

Help me, Sally.

Help me find Dick."

Jane said, "Oh, Father.

I can not find Dick.

And we can not play.

Help me, Father.

Help me find Dick."

Father said, "Look, Jane.

Look, look, look.

You can find Dick."

Sally said, "Oh, oh.

I see Dick now.

Father and I see Dick.

We see funny Dick.

Look, Jane, look.

You can find Dick now."

Who Can Help?

Dick said, "Mother, Mother.

Come here.

I want you.

Come and help me.

Oh, Jane.

Oh, Father.

Who can come?

Who can come and help me?"

Dick said, "Go away, Spot.

You can not help me.

Oh, my.

Oh, my.

I want Mother.

Mother can help me.

Run, Spot, run.

Run and find Mother."

Dick said, "Oh, Spot.
Now I can come in.
You can help me.
Little Spot can help.
You can help me come in."

See What I See

Dick said, "Look, Sally.

Look down here.

See what I see.

See my big cookie.

See me and my big cookie.

You can see Spot in here.

Spot wants my big cookie."

"Oh, oh," said Sally.
"I see Tim and me.
And now I see Puff.
Puff is in here.
I can see little Puff.
Puff and Tim and me."

Sally said, "Look, Jane.
Look down here.
You can see Jane in here."

Jane said, "Oh, oh, oh.
Who sees what I see?
It is something funny.
It is not Jane."

Little Boat

Sally said, "See my boat.

I want my little boat.

I want my little boat in here."

Jane said, "Dick can get it.

Dick is big.

Dick can go and get it."

"Not now," said Dick.

"I can not get it now."

Jane said, "Come, Sally.
Come and play.
Here is Tim."

"I want my boat," said Sally.
"Who can get it for me?
Is Father here?
Father can get it for me."

Sally said, "Oh, oh, oh.

Come here, Dick.

See what I see.

See my little blue boat now.

See who wants my boat.

My little blue boat.

See who wants it now."

What Can Dick Make?

Jane said, "Look, Sally.
See what I can make.
It is big and yellow.
It is for Puff."

Sally said, "Look, Mother.
I can make something for Tim.
Jane can make something for Puff.
What can Dick make?"

Dick said, "I can make something.
Come and see what it is."

"Is it blue?" said Sally.
"Is it yellow?
Is it red?"

Dick said, "Oh, my.
It is red and yellow and blue.
Come and see what it is."

Jane said, "Look, Sally.
Dick can make something pretty.
See what Dick can make."

"I see it," said Sally.
"It is pretty.
What is it?"

Jane said, "Oh, Sally.
It is **Dick**."

See It Go

Father said, "Look in here.
You can find something.
Something you want."

Dick said, "Look, Jane, look.
Red, yellow, and blue.
Yellow is for me.
Who wants red and blue?"

Jane said, "I want blue.
Red is for Sally."

Dick said, "Come, Sally.
Come and get something.
Red for you and blue for Jane."

Sally said, "Oh, Dick.
Pretty, pretty.
Make it big.
Make it big, big, big."

Jane said, "Run, Spot.
Run away, Puff.
See what I see.
Run, run, run."

"Now look," said Dick.

"See my boat.

See my boat go.

I can make it go away.

See it go.

Oh, see it go."

Who Can Work?

Dick said, "See me work.
I can help Father.
I can get something.
Something for Father."

Dick said, "Look, Father.

Jane plays and plays.

You and Mother work.

And I work.

Jane can not work.

Jane is a little baby."

Father said, "Oh, Dick.

Jane is not a baby."

Jane said, "See me now.

I can do something.

See me work.

I can help Mother.

See what I can do.

Sally is a baby.

Sally can not work."

Mother said, "Oh, my.
Sally is not here.
Who can find Sally?"

Sally said, "Look, Mother.
See me in my little house.
I can work.
And Spot and Puff can work.
We can make a house.
A funny little house."

Find My Ball

Sally said, "I want my ball.
My pretty yellow ball.
Who can find it for me?"

Jane said, "Here is a ball.
See this blue ball, Sally.
Do you want this ball?"

Sally said, "I want my ball.
My ball is yellow.
It is a big, pretty ball.
And it is in this house.
Help me find it."

"It is not here," said Dick.

Sally said, "Where is my ball?
It is in this house.
Where, oh, where is it?"

"It is not here," said Dick.
"Not down here, Sally."

Sally said, "Oh, Spot.
Do you see my ball?
Where is it, Spot?
Go and get it."

75

Sally said, "Oh, Jane.

Look up.

Look up.

See where my ball is.

Oh, oh, oh.

Dick looks down.

Little Spot looks up.

And Spot finds my ball.

My pretty yellow ball."

A Big Red Car

Dick said, "Away I go.
Away in my big red car.
See me go, Sally."

Sally said, "I want a car.

Make two cars, Dick.

A car for you.

And a car for me.

Make two cars."

Dick said, "Oh, Sally.

You can come in my car.

In my big red car."

"I want a car," said Sally.
"Make one for me, Dick.
A little one for me."

Dick said, "Look, Sally.
I can do something.
See what I can do.
I can make a big, big car.
Two can get in this car now."

Dick said, "Here, Sally.
This will look pretty in my car.
I will make it go up for you.
See it go up, up, up.
Now get in my car."

"Away we go," said Sally.
"Away, away in a big red car."

Who Will Jump?

Dick said, "Look, Sally.

Do you see this?

Come with me.

You will see something funny."

Sally said, "Oh, Dick.

I see what you want to do.

You want to make me jump.

Oh, oh.

You want to make me jump."

Dick said, "Not you, Sally.

I want to find Jane.

I want to make Jane jump."

Sally said, "I see Jane.
Jane is in the house.
Oh, oh.
I want to go in the house.
I want to see Jane jump."

"Come with me," said Dick.
"Come in the house with me.
You will see something funny.
You will see Jane jump."

Dick said, "Now look, Sally.
Now you will see Jane jump.
One.... Two...."

"Three," said Sally.
"One, two, three.
See Dick jump."

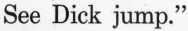

I See You

Jane said, "Come with me, Sally.
Come to the house with me.
Dick will not look here.
Not in the house.
Dick will not find you here."

Dick said, "Oh, oh.

I see something blue.

I can guess where Jane is.

One, two, three for Jane.

I see you, Jane.

One, two, three for you.

Come with me, Puff.

We want to find Sally now.

Where, oh, where is Sally?"

Dick said, "Oh, oh.

I see something yellow.

I can guess where Sally is.

One, two, three for Sally.

I see Sally with Jane.

One, two, three for Sally.

Now, little Puff.

Do you want to come with me?

We will get Jane and Sally."

Jane said, "One, two, three.
One, two, three for me.
And one, two, three for Sally.
Sally is with me."

Dick said, "Oh, funny me.
This is something yellow.
It is not Sally.
And this is something blue.
It is not Jane."

Guess Who

Sally said, "See the cars.

See the cars go up, up, up.

One, two, three.

Three little yellow cars."

Father said, "Oh, Baby Sally.
You can not play here.
This is where we work.
Here is a ball.
Run and play with the ball."

Mother said, "Spot, Spot.
Go to the house.
You can not play here.
Come with me to the house."

Jane said, "Come here, Dick.

Oh, come here.

Guess what I see.

Guess what Spot can make."

Sally said, "Oh, pretty, pretty.

Spot can make something pretty.

I can do what Spot can do.

I can make something pretty."

Jane said, "Oh, Father.
I want to do it."

Father said, "Come, Dick.
You and Jane can do it.
And here is little Puff.
I will help Puff do it."

Dick said, "Look, Mother.
See what we can make.
Guess who this is."

"Guess who this is," said Jane.

"Guess who this is," said Sally.
"And see the two little ones.
Guess who.
Guess who."

TO THE TEACHER

Guess Who, a special Junior Primer, provides an extra learning opportunity for those children who, after completing the three Pre-Primers of The New Basic Reading Program, *We Look and See, We Work and Play,* and *We Come and Go,* need additional help before beginning the Primer, *Fun with Dick and Jane.* A hard-bound book, similar in appearance to the Primer, *Guess Who* is more than "just another Pre-Primer." It represents a definite step forward. The accompanying *Guidebook* suggests procedures for meeting individual needs, especially those of the immature, or the frequently absent child. The *Think-and-Do Book* for *Guess Who* provides additional material to strengthen specific reading skills and to enable the child to maintain the abilities that will give him the confidence necessary for successful reading.

Guess Who has a total vocabulary of 68 words composed of the 58 words in the Pre-Primer Series and ten new words from the vocabulary of the first unit of The New Basic Primer. All 68 words are introduced gradually and are carefully maintained. No page introduces more than one word, and no story introduces more than four words. The ten new words are introduced in the second half of the book, at the rate of only one to a story.

The first five uses of each word are bunched for easy mastery; there is no gap of more than five pages between any two of these five uses. Thereafter, at spaced intervals, there are at least five more uses of each word. Thus, each of the 68 words is used a minimum of ten times.

At the end of each of the four sections of *Guess Who,* a review story repeats all words taught in that section, providing for the teacher an easy check on the child's progress.

All the words used in this Junior Primer are reintroduced and maintained in the Primer, *Fun with Dick and Jane.*

The 68 words used in *Guess Who* are listed on the following page. The ten words that are new in this book are printed in boldface type. Inflectional variants formed by adding *s* to a known root word are not listed.

Vocabulary List

5. Dick	25. Puff	45. find	69. work
6. look	26. here	46. me	70. a
7. oh	27. jump	47. father	71. **do**
8. see	28. can	48. **now**	72. house
9. Sally	29. go	49. **who**	73. ball
10. Jane	30. play	50. want	74. **this**
11. little	31. mother	51. my	75. where
12. funny	32. down	52. in	76. up
13. help	33. Tim	53. **what**	77. car
14. Spot	34. said	54. big	78. two
15. come	35. cookies	55. is	79. one
16. and	36. we	56. it	80. **will**
17. something	37. away	57. boat	81. **with**
18.	38. not	58. **get**	82. to
19. I	39. you	59. for	83. the
20. baby	40. run	60. blue	84. three
21.	41.	61. make	85. . . . . .
22.	42.	62. yellow	86. **guess**
23.	43.	63. red	87. . . . . .
24.	44.	64. **pretty**	88. . . . . .
		65.	89. . . . . .
		66.	90. . . . . .
		67.	91. . . . . .
		68.	92. . . . . .
			93. . . . . .